Scottish Slimmers

cool

contents

Key to recipes

All values given in the recipes are for calories, Checks and grams of fat (in that order), excluding No-Check foods, and are **per serving** unless stated otherwise.

two | 000 | 0 0

Checks

Calories   Fat
                 grams

chill
out

SERVES **four** 50 **2** ② chilled tomato soup with garlic croûtons

Prep: **10** mins   Cook: **40** mins   Chill: **3-4** hrs

- 1 onion, finely chopped
- 2 carrots, diced
- 2 garlic cloves, crushed
- 1 teaspoon olive oil
- 900 g/2 lb ripe tomatoes, skinned and chopped
- 600 ml/1 pint chicken or vegetable stock
- few sprigs of fresh thyme, chopped
- salt and freshly ground black pepper
- thyme sprigs to garnish

Garlic croûtons:
- 3 thin slices French bread (baguette)
- spray oil
- 1 garlic clove, halved

1 Gently sweat the onion, carrots and garlic in the olive oil over a low heat until soft, about 10 minutes. Add the tomatoes and cook gently for a further 10 minutes until the juices start to reduce.

2 Add the stock and chopped thyme and simmer for 10-15 minutes. Remove from the heat and cool slightly.

3 Purée half the soup in a blender or food processor and then mix with the remaining unpurÈed soup. Season to taste with salt and pepper and chill in the refrigerator.

4 Shortly before serving, spray the French bread lightly with spray oil and place on a hot ridged grill pan or under an overhead grill. Cook for about 2 minutes each side until crisp and golden. Rub each slice with the cut garlic cloves and cut the bread into cubes.

5 Serve the soup topped with the croûtons, garnished with sprigs of thyme.

spiced green pea soup

Prep: **10** mins   Cook: **30** mins   Chill: **3-4** hrs

1 onion, chopped
1 medium potato, peeled and diced
2 garlic cloves, crushed
2.5 cm/1 in piece fresh root ginger, peeled and chopped
1 teaspoon ground cumin
½ teaspoon coriander seeds, crushed
900 ml/1½ pints hot vegetable stock
225 g/8 oz frozen peas
1 fresh chilli, deseeded and chopped
juice of ½ lemon
few coriander leaves, chopped
salt and freshly ground black pepper
150 ml/¼ pint very low-fat yoghurt
fresh coriander, to garnish

1 Put the onion, potato, garlic, ginger, spices and stock in a large saucepan and bring to the boil. Cover the pan and simmer for 25 minutes.

2 Stir in the peas and chilli, then bring back to the boil before lowering the heat and cooking for 5 more minutes until all the vegetables are tender.

3 Add the lemon juice and chopped coriander and season to taste.

4 Purée the soup in batches until smooth in a blender or food processor, and then chill in the refrigerator.

5 Just before serving, swirl in the yogurt. Spoon into serving bowls and top each one with a sprig of coriander.

moorish cucumber & yoghurt soup

SERVES six | 35 | 1.5 0

Prep: **30** mins Chill: **3-4** hrs

2 cucumbers, peeled, deseeded and diced
salt
225 g/8 oz Total 0% fat Greek yoghurt
250 ml/8 fl oz tomato juice
600 ml/1 pint vegetable stock
3 tablespoons chopped fresh mint
Tabasco sauce to taste
salt and freshly ground black pepper
chopped fresh coriander to garnish

1 Put the diced cucumber in a colander and then sprinkle about 1 tablespoon salt over it. Set aside to drain for about 30 minutes before rinsing the cucumber well under running cold water and patting dry with kitchen paper.

2 Meanwhile, put the yoghurt in a bowl and stir in the tomato juice and stock. Add 1 tablespoon chopped mint and set aside.

3 Strain the yoghurt mixture through a sieve and stir in the cucumber, remaining mint and Tabasco to taste. Go easy on it, adding just a few drops at a time.

4 Chill in the refrigerator until you are ready to serve. Check the seasoning, spoon into serving bowls and sprinkle with coriander.

vichyssoise

six   65    2.5 0

Prep: **10** mins Cook: **30** mins Chill: **3-4** hrs

3 leeks, trimmed, sliced and washed
1 small onion, finely chopped
spray oil
225 g/8 oz potatoes, peeled and diced
600 ml/1 pint chicken or vegetable stock
pinch of grated nutmeg
150 ml/5 fl oz low-fat natural yoghurt
salt and freshly ground black pepper
fresh chives, to garnish

1 Sweat the leeks and onion in a hot pan that has been lightly sprayed with oil. Cook gently, stirring frequently to prevent sticking, for about 10 minutes until softened.

2 Add the potatoes, stock and nutmeg and bring to the boil. Cover the pan, reduce the heat to a simmer and cook for 20 minutes until all the vegetables are tender.

3 Purée until smooth in a blender or food processor and set aside to cool. When cold, stir in the yoghurt and season taste with salt and pepper.

4 Chill in the refrigerator until ready to serve. Pour into bowls and serve garnished with snipped chives.

SERVES
two   No-Check

roast baby leeks vinaigrette

Prep: **10** mins Cook: **20-25** mins

- **175 g/6 oz baby leeks**
- **1 red onion, cut into wedges**
- **115 g/4 oz cherry tomatoes**
- **spray oil**
- **sea salt and freshly ground black pepper**
- **3 tablespoons oil-free vinaigrette dressing**
- **2 tablespoons finely chopped parsley**

1 Wash the baby leeks and trim the ends. Pat dry with kitchen paper and arrange them in an ovenproof dish.

2 Place the red onion wedges and baby tomatoes around the sides of the dish and spray with spray oil. Sprinkle with a little sea salt and grind over some black pepper.

3 Roast in a preheated oven at 180°C/Gas Mark 4 for 20-25 minutes, until the leeks and onions are tender.

4 Drizzle the vinaigrette over the hot vegetables and set aside to cool. Serve lukewarm or chilled, scattered with chopped parsley.

smoked trout with tapenade salad

two | 6 4

Prep: **15** mins

2 x 75 g/2½ oz smoked trout fillets
75 g/2½ oz Total 0% fat Greek yoghurt
1 teaspoon horseradish sauce
squeeze of lemon juice
salt and freshly ground black pepper

Tapenade salad:
4 spring onions, trimmed and sliced diagonally
4 cherry tomatoes, halved
8 small black olives in brine, drained, pitted and chopped
8 small green olives in brine, drained, pitted and chopped
½ yellow pepper, deseeded and chopped
few sprigs of mint, roughly chopped
juice of ½ lemon
2 tablespoons oil-free vinaigrette dressing

1 Make the tapenade salad by mixing together the spring onions, tomatoes, olives and pepper in a bowl. Add the mint, sprinkle over the lemon juice and toss lightly in the dressing.

2 Divide the salad between 2 serving plates. Add a smoked trout to each one.

3 Mix together the yoghurt, horseradish and lemon juice and arrange a swirl of this on each serving plate. Check the seasoning and serve.

cool
salads

205 8 6 prosciutto chicken with red pepper salad

SERVES: two

Prep: **10** mins Cook: **25** mins

2 x 125 g/4½ oz boneless chicken breasts, skinned
2 sage leaves
2 sun-dried tomatoes, sliced
4 thin slices Parma ham, visible fat removed
spray oil

Red pepper salad:
2 large red peppers
1 garlic clove, crushed
1 teaspoon oil-free vinaigrette dressing
sea salt and freshly ground black pepper

1 Spread the chicken breasts out on a board and, with a sharp knife, make a thin slit in the centre of each one to create a 'pocket'. Tuck a sage leaf and sliced sun-dried tomato into each chicken breast.

2 Spread out 2 slices of Parma ham and wrap a stuffed chicken breast tightly inside them. Do the same with the remaining chicken breast.

3 Spray lightly with oil and cook in a hot pan over a medium heat for about 20 minutes, turning frequently until golden brown all over and the chicken is cooked through. Leave to cool, overnight if wished.

4 Place the red peppers under a hot grill and cook, turning them often, until charred and blistered all over. Place them in a plastic bag for a few minutes to help loosen the skin and then peel. Remove the seeds and cut the flesh into strips.

5 Mix the strips of pepper with the crushed garlic and dressing. Add a little sea salt and black pepper to taste. Serve with the cold chicken breasts, either whole or sliced.

vietnamese beef salad

SERVES two 225 9 7

Prep: **10** mins Cook: **6-8** mins

2 x 150 g/5 oz lean sirloin steaks, all visible fat removed
salt and freshly ground black pepper
small packet of salad leaves
few sprigs of coriander, chopped
few sprigs of mint, chopped
¼ cucumber, cut into matchstick strips
1 small carrot, cut into thin matchstick strips
4 cherry tomatoes, quartered

Spicy dressing:
juice of 1 lime
2 tablespoons nam pla (Thai fish sauce)
1 tablespoon sweet chilli sauce
1 red bird's eye chilli, deseeded and finely chopped (optional)

1 Make the spicy dressing by mixing all the ingredients together in a small bowl. Only use the fresh chilli if you like really hot food. Set aside.

2 Sprinkle the steaks with salt and pepper and cook for 3-4 minutes each side on a really hot ridged cast iron grill pan. They should be browned on the outside with attractive singed stripes but still slightly pink inside.
If you like your steaks well done, cook them for a little longer. Cut into thin strips.

3 Meanwhile, mix together all the salad ingredients and toss lightly in the spicy dressing. Pile on to 2 serving plates and arrange the hot strips of steak on top.

SERVES two | 210 8 8 **bresaola & rocket salad with parmesan**

Prep: **10** mins Cook: **5** mins

75 g/2½ oz thinly sliced bresaola (dry-cured beef)
60 g/2 oz wild rocket
1 tablespoon oil-free vinaigrette dressing
good squeeze of lemon juice
freshly ground black pepper
30 g/1 oz Parmesan cheese
segments of ruby-red orange, to garnish

Garlic lemon croûtes:
½ teaspoon crushed garlic
1 teaspoon finely chopped parsley
grated zest of 1 lemon
½ teaspoon olive oil
2 thin slices french bread (baguette)

1 Prepare the garlic lemon croûtes. Mix together the garlic, parsley, lemon zest and olive oil. Spread over the French bread and cook on a baking sheet in a preheated oven at 200°C/Gas Mark 6 for 5 minutes until crisp and golden.

2 Arrange the bresaola and rocket on 2 serving plates. Drizzle with the dressing and lemon juice, and add a good grinding of black pepper.

3 Shave the Parmesan over the top, using a potato peeler to produce large slivers. Garnish with the orange segments and serve with the garlic lemon croûtes.

parma ham & poached egg salad

Prep: **10** mins   Cook: **4** mins

2 large free-range eggs
75 g/2½ oz wafer-sliced Parma ham, visible fat removed
spray oil
115 g/4 oz button mushrooms, thinly sliced
small packet prepared mixed leaf salad
few baby spinach leaves
salt and freshly ground black pepper
1 tablespoon oil-free vinaigrette dressing

1 Poach the eggs in an egg poacher or break them into a small pan of boiling water and cover and simmer for 3-4 minutes.

2 Meanwhile, dry-fry the slices of Parma ham for 1 minute each side until crisp and golden.

3 Spray a pan lightly with oil and sauté the mushrooms quickly until golden.

4 Arrange the salad and spinach leaves on 2 plates with the Parma ham and mushrooms on top. Season lightly and sprinkle with vinaigrette.

5 Place a warm poached egg on top of each serving and eat immediately.

165 7 2 tuscan rustic salad

SERVES two

Prep: **10** mins Cook: **10** mins

2 slices ciabatta
spray olive oil
200g can tuna chunks in brine, drained
6 ripe cherry tomatoes, halved
½ small cucumber, peeled and cut into chunks
½ red onion, chopped
½ red pepper, deseeded and chopped
1 tablespoon capers, rinsed
small handful of fresh parsley and basil, chopped
1 garlic clove
1 mild red chilli, deseeded and finely chopped
2 tablespoons oil-free vinaigrette dressing
salt and freshly ground black pepper

1 Tear the ciabatta roughly into bite-sized chunks on a baking tray and spray lightly with oil. Bake in a preheated oven at 200°C/Gas Mark 6 for about 10 minutes until golden brown.

2 Place in a salad bowl with the tuna, tomatoes, cucumber, red onion, pepper, capers and chopped herbs.

3 Crush the garlic clove and chilli in a pestle and mortar and blend in the vinaigrette. Toss the salad in this dressing, then check the seasoning and serve.

thai griddled
chicken salad

Prep: **10** mins   Cook: **20** mins

2 x 125 g/4½ oz boneless chicken breasts, skinned
spray oil
1 carrot, cut into thin matchstick strips
3 spring onions, trimmed and sliced diagonally
¼ cucumber, cut into matchstick strips
60 g/2 oz bean sprouts
small bunch of watercress, trimmed and washed

Thai citrus dressing:
2 tablespoons nam pla (Thai fish sauce)
juice of 1 lime
1 red bird's eye chilli, deseeded and finely chopped
1 garlic clove, crushed
1 teaspoon brown sugar
1 tablespoon chopped coriander

1 Spray the chicken breasts lightly with oil and cook on a hot ridged grill pan for about 10 minutes each side until cooked through and attractively striped.

2 Put the carrot strips, spring onions, cucumber, bean sprouts and watercress in a serving bowl. Cut the chicken into strips and arrange on top.

3 Heat the nam pla, lime juice, chilli, garlic and sugar in a small pan, stirring until the sugar dissolves. Add the coriander and pour over the salad. Serve straight away.

really
cool

salmon & coriander fishcakes

Prep: **10** mins Cook: **25** mins

250 g/9 oz potatoes, peeled and cut up roughly
1 tablespoon very low-fat natural yogurt
250 g/9 oz cooked or canned salmon
1 small green chilli, deseeded and chopped (optional)
few drops of nam pla (Thai fish sauce, optional)
2 tablespoons chopped fresh coriander
salt and freshly ground black pepper
flour for dusting
spray oil
lemon wedges or chilli sauce, to serve

1 Cook the potatoes in a pan of salted boiling water until just tender. Drain and mash until smooth with the yoghurt.

2 Flake the cooked or canned salmon and mix in the potato mixture. If wished, flavour with chopped chilli and nam pla, then stir in the coriander and season with salt and pepper.

3 Chill the mixture for 5 minutes in the refrigerator and then shape with your hands into 6 patties and dust lightly with flour.

4 Spray a frying pan with oil and place over a medium heat. When hot, add the fishcakes and cook for 4-5 minutes each side until golden.

5 Serve with lemon wedges and a crisp salad or some sweet chilli sauce (1 Check 0g fat per dessertspoon) and steamed green vegetables.

SERVES two 370 15 10

cherry tomato & angel hair pasta

Prep: **5** mins   Cook: **15** mins

- **2 teaspoons olive oil**
- **2 garlic cloves, chopped**
- **1 red chilli, deseeded and finely chopped (optional)**
- **2 tablespoons tomato purée**
- **12 really ripe cherry tomatoes**
- **few drops of balsamic vinegar**
- **few sprigs of fresh basil, torn**
- **salt and freshly ground black pepper**
- **175 g/6 oz angel hair pasta (dry weight)**
- **15 g/½ oz Parmesan shavings**
- **sprigs of basil, to garnish**

1 Heat the oil in a large frying pan and gently cook the garlic and chilli until soft over a really low heat.

2 Add the tomato purée and cherry tomatoes, turn up the heat and cook for 5 minutes or so, until the tomatoes have softened. Squash some of them with the back of a wooden spoon if wished to thicken the sauce. Add the balsamic vinegar and basil and let it reduce a bit more for 2-3 minutes. Season to taste.

3 Meanwhile, cook the pasta in a large pan of lightly salted water, according to the manufacturer's instructions, until just tender (al dente).

4 Drain well and return the pasta to the empty hot pan. Pour in the sauce and stir gently until lightly coated. Serve sprinkled with Parmesan shavings and fresh basil.

sautéed scallops with chorizo salsa

SERVES **two** 215 **9** ⑧

Prep: **10** mins Cook: **6** mins

8 large scallops
spray oil
crlsp lettuce or curly endive (frisée)
chopped parsley, to garnish
salt and freshly ground black pepper
lime quarters, to garnish

Chorizo salsa:

60 g/2 oz chorizo, skinned and diced
½ red onion, finely chopped
½ red pepper, deseeded and chopped
2 ripe tomatoes, skinned and chopped
1 garlic clove, crushed
juice of ½ lime

1 Make the chorizo salsa. Heat a frying pan and, when really hot, add the chorizo. Cook for 2-3 minutes, stirring, until the oil starts to run out.

2 Drain off the oil and mix the chorizo with the red onion, pepper, tomatoes, garlic and lime juice. Cover and set aside until required.

3 Cook the scallops until golden in a frying pan that has been sprayed lightly with oil. They will only need about 1-2 minutes each side or they will lose their moist tenderness.

4 Arrange the cooked scallops on top of the lettuce or endive. Scatter with parsley and grind some salt and pepper over the top. Serve with the lime wedges and chorizo salsa.

SERVES two | 270 **11** **16** baked swordfish
with low-fat guacamole

Prep: **10** mins Cook: **15-20** mins

2 x 175 g/6 oz swordfish steaks
grated zest and juice of 1 lime
few sprigs of fresh mint, chopped
sea salt and freshly ground black pepper

Low-fat guacamole:

1 small ripe avocado, peeled and stoned
1 tablespoon very low-fat fromage frais
1 ripe, tomato, skinned, deseeded and chopped
1 small red chilli, deseeded and finely chopped
1 tablespoon chopped fresh coriander
salt and pepper

1 Place the swordfish steaks on a rectangle of foil and
squeeze the lime juice over the top. Scatter with the
grated zest and chopped mint, then season lightly. Pull
up the foil and twist the ends to form a neat parcel and
place on a baking sheet.

2 Bake in a preheated oven at 200°C/Gas Mark 6 for
15-20 minutes until the swordfish is cooked and tender.

3 While the swordfish is cooking, make the guacamole.
Mash the avocado flesh in a bowl with the fromage
frais and mix in the tomato, chilli and coriander. Check
the seasoning.

4 Remove the cooked fish from the foil and serve with a
spoonful of guacamole and some cooked vegetables,
such as green beans, mangetout, broccoli florets or
baby carrots.

spicy pork steaks with mango

Prep: **10** mins Chill: **10-15** mins Cook: **15** mins

2 x 150 g/5 oz pork loin steaks, all visible fat removed
juice of 1 lime or lemon
½ small red chilli, deseeded and finely chopped
1 garlic clove, crushed
spray oil
1 red onion, cut into wedges

Mango garnish:
1 ripe mango, peeled, stoned and diced
½ red pepper, deseeded and diced
½ small red chilli, deseeded and finely chopped
grated zest and juice of 1 lime or lemon
2 tablespoons chopped fresh coriander
salt and pepper

1 Put the pork steaks in a dish with the lime or lemon juice, chilli and crushed garlic. Coat well and set aside in a cool place for 10-15 minutes.

2 Spray a griddle pan with oil and place over a medium to high heat. Add the pork steaks and red onion wedges and cook for about 15 minutes, turning occasionally, until the steaks are cooked through and the onions are tender and charred.

3 Meanwhile, mix all the ingredients for the mango garnish, seasoning to taste.

4 Serve the pork topped with a spoonful of the mango garnish. Plain boiled rice (4 Checks 1g fat per 30g dry weight/75g boiled weight) and salad make a good accompaniment.

SERVES two | 21 5 9 18 **herby cheese stuffed romano peppers**

Prep: **5** mins Cook: **12** mins

4 romano peppers (or sweet red ones), halved and deseeded
spray olive oil
100 g/3½ oz soft goat's cheese
1 tablespoon chopped fresh parsley
1 tablespoon snipped chives
salt and freshly ground black pepper
2 teaspoons pesto sauce

1 Cook the halved peppers on a hot griddle pan or under an overhead grill until the skin is slightly charred and the flesh is softened.

2 While the peppers are cooking, mix together the goat's cheese, chopped herbs and seasoning to taste.

3 Smear the pesto sauce lightly inside each hot pepper and then top with the herby cheese mixture. Pop the peppers back on the griddle or under the grill for 2-3 minutes to heat through and then serve with some couscous (4 Checks 0g fat per 30g dry weight/ 75g steamed weight) and grilled mushrooms.

SERVES **two** 170 **7** 9

japanese vegetable stacks

Prep: **15** mins Cook: **20** mins

spray oil
1 aubergine, sliced into thick rings
1 beef tomato, cut into rings
4 thin slices halloumi cheese
1 tablespoon teriyaki sauce
1 teaspoon rice vinegar
½ teaspoon liquid honey
1 tablespoon finely chopped coriander
salt and freshly ground black pepper
¼ teaspoon toasted sesame seeds
whole chives, to garnish

Piquant tomato sauce:
1 small onion, finely chopped
1 garlic clove, crushed
115 g/4 oz ripe tomatoes, skinned and finely chopped
60 ml/2 fl oz red wine
1 teaspoon balsamic vinegar
salt and freshly ground black pepper

1 Make the tomato sauce. Cook the onion and garlic gently in a pan that has been sprayed lightly with oil. Add half of the chopped tomatoes and the wine and cook for 5 minutes. Purée until smooth in a blender and then stir in the remaining chopped tomatoes and balsamic vinegar. Season with salt and pepper to taste.

2 Spray a ridged cast iron griddle pan with oil. Place over a medium heat and cook the aubergine until just tender and striped on both sides. Add the tomato slices and halloumi cheese and sear gently.

3 On 2 individual serving plates, layer up the griddled aubergine, tomato and halloumi slices.

4 Blend together the teriyaki sauce, rice vinegar, honey and seasoning and dribble over the vegetable stacks. Sprinkle with sesame seeds. Pour the tomato sauce around them on the plates and garnish with chives.

filo tartlets with caramelized vegetables

two | 5

Prep: **15** mins Cook: **20** mins

4 x 15 g/½ oz sheets filo pastry
1 egg white, lightly beaten
2 small red onions, thinly sliced
1 small red pepper, deseeded and sliced
1 small yellow pepper, deseeded and sliced
3 tablespoons red wine
1 tablespoon wine vinegar
1 teaspoon liquid honey
salt and freshly ground black pepper
2 heaped teaspoons very low-fat fromage frais
snipped chives, to garnish

1 Cut a 15 cm/6 in square out of each filo sheet. Drape 2 of the squares over 2 large tartlet tins and press them in slightly. Brush with beaten egg white and then place another filo square on top at a slight angle to produce a ragged star shape.

2 Bake the pastry tartlets in a preheated oven at 180°C/Gas Mark 4 for about 5 minutes until crisp and golden. Do not overcook.

3 Put the red onions, peppers, wine and vinegar in a pan and cook over a gentle heat until the vegetables are softened and caramelized and the liquid has reduced. Stir in the honey and season with salt and pepper to taste.

4 Pile the caramelized vegetables into the tartlet cases. Top each one with a swirl of fromage frais and a sprinkling of chives. Serve with a crisp salad.

SERVES **two** | 150 **6** 11

chargrilled asparagus with parmesan

Prep: **10** mins Cook: **10** mins

1 bunch asparagus
olive oil spray
30 g/1 oz Parmesan cheese
salt and freshly ground black pepper

Honey mustard dressing:
1 tablespoon olive oil
1 teaspoon cider vinegar
juice of 1 orange
juice of 1 lemon
1 teaspoon whole-grain mustard
1 teaspoon honey

1 Trim the woody ends from the asparagus spears. Half-fill a large pan with salted water and bring to the boil. Drop in the asparagus and blanch for 3-4 minutes.

2 Carefully remove the asparagus and pat dry with kitchen paper.

3 Make the dressing: mix together all the ingredients and keep stirring vigorously until the mixture emulsifies.

4 Heat a ridged cast iron grill pan which has been sprayed lightly with oil. When it is really hot, gently lay the asparagus in the pan. As soon as they start to colour, turn them so that they cook evenly all over.

5 Arrange the asparagus on a serving dish and drizzle with the honey mustard dressing. Using a potato peeler, shave the Parmesan over the top and season with salt and pepper. Serve hot or cold.

griddled halloumi & chickpea salad

Prep: **15** mins Cook: **3-4** mins

1 red onion, finely chopped
2 ripe tomatoes, chopped
8 black olives, pitted and chopped
200 g/7 oz canned chick peas, drained
few sprigs of mint, chopped
few sprigs of parsley, chopped
grated zest of 1 lemon
3 tablespoons oil-free French dressing
juice of 1 lemon
125 g/4½ oz halloumi cheese, sliced
cos lettuce leaves
salt and freshly ground black pepper

1 Mix together the red onion, tomatoes, olives, chick peas and chopped herbs in a bowl. Sprinkle with the lemon zest.

2 Mix the French dressing and lemon juice and use to toss the chick pea mixture.

3 Place the slices of halloumi cheese on a hot ridged griddle pan and dry-fry for 3-4 minutes, turning frequently, until the cheese is attractively striped and golden.

4 Arrange some cos lettuce leaves on 2 serving plates and spoon the chick pea salad over them. Top with the slices of hot griddled halloumi cheese. Sprinkle with some salt and black pepper and serve.

SERVES **two** No-Check

californian barbecued salad

Prep: **10** mins Cook: **5** mins

spray olive oil
125 g/4½ oz asparagus, trimmed
1 courgette, sliced diagonally
½ red pepper, deseeded and cut into strips
½ yellow pepper, deseeded and cut into strips
4 fat spring onions, trimmed and halved
**small bag of crisp salad leaves, e.g. radicchio, curly
endive, rocket, spinach**
3 tablespoons oil-free vinaigrette dressing
salt and freshly ground black pepper
few sprigs of basil
1 orange, segmented, to garnish

1 Heat a barbecue and oil the bars or, if you are
cooking inside, spray a ridged griddle pan with
oil. When the grill is really hot, add the asparagus,
courgette, peppers and spring onions. Cook over
a medium to high heat, turning frequently, until the
vegetables are tender and just starting to char.
Remove.

2 Tip the salad leaves onto the hot grill and toss
quickly over the heat - just long enough to warm and
wilt them.

3 Toss the barbecued vegetables and salad leaves in
the dressing. Season with salt and add a good grinding
of black pepper. Strew with basil and garnish with
orange segments. Serve warm.

note...

Count 1 Check if you eat the orange garnish!

honey-roasted vegetables with polenta

two

Prep: **10** mins Cook: **15-20** mins

spray oil
1 red onion, cut into small wedges
1 large carrot, peeled and cut into chunks
1 yellow pepper, deseeded and cut into squares
1 small bulb fennel, trimmed and cut into small wedges
2 garlic cloves
few sprigs of thyme and rosemary
sea salt and freshly ground black pepper
1 teaspoon liquid honey
60 g/2 oz instant polenta

1 Spray a roasting pan with oil and arrange the red onion, carrot, yellow pepper and fennel in the pan. Tuck the unpeeled garlic cloves in among the vegetables and sprinkle with thyme and rosemary sprigs and seasoning. Drizzle the honey over the top.

2 Bake in a preheated oven at 180°C/Gas Mark 4 for 15-20 minutes, turning the vegetables over occasionally.

3 Discard any sprigs of herb that are charred. Peel the garlic cloves and squeeze the garlic over he roasted vegetables.

4 While the vegetables are roasting, cook the polenta according to the packet instructions. Spoon the cooked polenta into a neat round on each serving plate and top with the honey-roasted vegetables.

SERVES **four** | 70 **3** **0**

summer berry wine jelly terrine

Prep: **15** mins Chill: **Overnight**

- 1 sachet sugar-free raspberry jelly crystals
- 285 ml/9 fl oz boiling water
- 285 ml/9 fl oz sparkling white or rosé wine
- 125 g/4½ oz raspberries
- 125 g/4½ oz blueberries or redcurrants
- 125 g/4½ oz strawberries, hulled and halved
- 125 g/4½ oz ripe cherries, pitted
- Total 0% fat Greek yoghurt, to serve

1 Make up the raspberry jelly. Sprinkle the contents of the sachet onto the boiling water and stir thoroughly until completely dissolved.

2 Add the sparkling wine, stirring all the time and then pour a little into the base of a 900 g/2 lb loaf tin or mould.

3 Layer the soft fruits in the tin or mould and then pour the remaining jelly over the top.

4 Cover with clingfilm and place in the refrigerator overnight until chilled and set solid.

5 To turn out the jelly terrine, dip the base of the tin or mould very quickly into hot water and invert it onto a serving dish. Served sliced with some Greek yogurt.

apricots
with star anise

SERVES two | 120 5 2

Prep: **5** mins Infuse: **5** mins Cook: **30-40** mins

- **250 g/9 oz ripe apricots**
- **2 star anise**
- **2 lemon and ginger tea bags**
- **1 tablespoon caster sugar**
- **125 ml/4½ fl oz low-fat apricot yoghurt**

1 Cut each apricot in half and remove the stone. Arrange them in the base of an ovenproof dish, cut-side up, and tuck in the star anise.

2 Bring a kettle of water to the boil and pour out 350 ml/12 fl oz into a measuring bowl or jug. Add the tea bags and leave to infuse for about 5 minutes.

3 Remove the tea bags and stir in the sugar until thoroughly dissolved. Pour over the apricots.

4 Bake in a preheated oven at 180°C/Gas Mark 4 for 30-40 minutes, until the apricots are cooked and tender but still hold their shape.

5 Cool and then chill in the refrigerator until required. Serve with low-fat apricot yoghurt.

chilled moroccan peaches

Prep: **10** mins Chill: **2-3** hrs Cook: **2-3** mins

2 large ripe peaches
2 teaspoons rosewater
100 ml/3½ fl oz low-fat natural yoghurt
2 teaspoons caster sugar
sprigs of mint, to decorate

1 Wash the peaches and pat dry with kitchen paper. Cut each one in half and carefully remove the stone.

2 Slice each peach into a small but deep heatproof dish and sprinkle with the rosewater. Cover and chill in the refrigerator for at least 2 hours.

3 Spoon the yoghurt over the peaches and sprinkle with the sugar.

4 Heat an overhead grill until it is red hot and place the dishes underneath. Leave for 2-3 minutes until the sugar melts and caramelizes.

5 Let the dishes cool and then pop back into the fridge until the caramel topping is really cold and crisp. Serve decorated with sprigs of mint.

scarlet fruit
salad with wine

Prep: **10** mins Chill: **3** hrs

- **125 g/4½ oz strawberries**
- **125 g/4½ oz raspberries**
- **125 g/4½ oz cherries, pitted**
- **60 g/2 oz blueberries**
- **1 tablespoon vanilla or caster sugar**
- **125 ml/4½ fl oz rosé wine**
- **2 x 60 ml scoops frozen strawberry yogurt**

1 Hull the strawberries and, if large, cut into halves or quarters. Place them in a bowl with the raspberries, cherries and blueberries.

2 Sprinkle with sugar and pour the wine over the top. Cover and chill in the refrigerator for at least 3 hours or overnight.

3 To serve, place a scoop of frozen yogurt in each of 2 tall glasses, then top with the chilled fruit salad. Serve immediately.

SERVES
two 165 **7** 1

mini summer puddings

Prep: **15** mins Cook: **10** mins Chill: **Overnight**

- **60 g/2 oz redcurrants**
- **60 g/2 oz blackcurrants**
- **125 g/4½ oz raspberries**
- **1 tablespoon icing sugar**
- **4 thin slices white bread**
- **mint leaves, to garnish**
- **virtually fat-free fromage frais, to serve**

1 Put the redcurrants, blackcurrants and raspberries in a pan with the icing sugar. Stir gently over a low heat to dissolve the sugar and then simmer for about 10 minutes until the fruit softens and the juices run.

2 Trim the crusts from the bread and flatten with a rolling pin. Cut the bread into suitable shapes to line 2 ramekin dishes, reserving some for the 'lids'.

3 Fill with the stewed summer fruits and their juices, then cover with the remaining bread and wrap each ramekin tightly in clingfilm.

4 Place a saucer on top and then a heavy weight or unopened can. Leave in the refrigerator to chill overnight.

5 To serve, remove the clingfilm and run the point of a sharp knife around the inside of each ramekin to loosen the pudding. Place a serving plate on top and then invert the ramekin to turn out the pudding on to the plate. Decorate with mint leaves and serve with fromage frais.

gooseberry & elderflower fool

two   7

Prep: **10** mins Cook: **10** mins Chill: **1-2** hrs

250 g/9 oz gooseberries
30 g/1 oz caster sugar
1 tablespoon elderflower cordial (e.g. Bottlegreen)
150 ml/¼ pint Total 0% fat Greek yoghurt
low-fat yoghurt and mint sprigs, to decorate

1 Top and tail the gooseberries and put them into a stainless steel pan. Add 1 tablespoon water and cook gently over a very low heat for about 10 minutes until they are softened and yellow.

2 Crush the gooseberries with a fork if you want a textured fool; alternatively, you can purée them in a blender or food processor until thick and smooth.

3 Stir in the sugar and elderflower cordial and then set aside to cool.

4 When cool, spoon the Greek yoghurt into a bowl and gently swirl in the gooseberry purée. Divide between 2 serving glasses or dishes and chill until required. Serve topped with a swirl of yoghurt and a sprig of mint.

note...

Caster sugar may be replaced by 2 tablespoons granulated sweetener. This will reduce values to 105 calories, 4 Checks, 1 fat gram.

ice
cool

blueberry yoghurt ice

| four | 160 | 6 3 |

Prep: **10** mins Cook: **10** mins Freeze: **4+** hrs

- **250 g/9 oz blueberries**
- **30 g/1 oz sugar**
- **350 ml/12 fl oz low-fat natural yoghurt**
- **4 waffle cones or baskets**

1 Put the blueberries in a saucepan with the sugar and 1 tablespoon water. Bring to the boil, stirring to dissolve the sugar, and then reduce the heat to a bare simmer.

2 Cook the blueberries gently for about 10 minutes, stirring frequently, until they soften and burst, releasing their coloured juice. Remove from the heat and leave to cool.

3 When the blueberries are cold, swirl in the yoghurt. You can mix it to a uniform colour or stop in time to produce an attractive rippled effect.

4 Pour into a plastic container and cover with a lid or some clingfilm. Freeze for at least 1 hour until the edges are frozen.

5 Remove from the freezer and beat the blueberry mixture to break up the ice crystals. Cover the container and replace in the freezer for another hour and then repeat the process, and then do the same again - you will need to beat and freeze it 3 times for a really smooth result. Alternatively, if you have an ice cream maker, it will do this for you.

6 Remove from the freezer at least 10-15 minutes before serving to allow the ice to soften. Scoop it out and serve in waffle cones or baskets.

raspberry meringue ice cream cake

SERVES four | 200 8 3

Prep: **20** mins Freeze: **3+** hrs

- spray oil
- 6 small meringue nests
- 400 ml/14 fl oz Carte d'Or Light Vanilla Ice Cream
- 125 g/4½ oz raspberries

Raspberry coulis:
- 250 g/9 oz raspberries, reserving a few for decoration
- 1 tablespoon icing sugar, sifted

1 Spray a mist of oil into a 450 g/1 lb loaf tin and brush around the sides and base. Measure and cut out a piece of greaseproof paper or baking parchment to fit into the base of the tin.

2 Roughly break 2 of the meringue nests into large pieces and arrange them in the base. Cover with half of the ice cream, pressing down firmly, and all the raspberries.

3 Break up 2 more meringue nests and scatter them over the raspberries. Cover with the remaining ice cream and press down well. Scatter the rest of the meringue on top.

4 Cover with a piece of baking parchment which has been cut to fit and then wrap the loaf tin in foil. Press down again on the top to level it. Place in the freezer for at least 3 hours or, preferably, overnight.

5 Before serving, make the raspberry coulis. You can either push the raspberries through a nylon sieve, pressing down with a spoon, and then discard the pips, or you can blitz them in a blender and then sieve them. Sweeten with the icing sugar.

6 Remove the foil and paper from the loaf tin and run a knife around the sides of the ice cream cake to loosen. Turn out by inverting it onto a plate and cut into slices.

7 Serve each slice sitting in a little pool of coulis with a few of the reserved raspberries for decoration.

iced strawberry terrine

Prep: **20** mins Freeze: **5+** hrs

- **450 g/1 lb ripe strawberries, hulled**
- **2 tablespoons icing sugar**
- **1 tablespoon Cointreau**
- **500 g pot virtually fat-free fromage frais**
- **75 g/2½ oz Italian ratafia biscuits, roughly crushed**
- **a few whole strawberries, to decorate**

1 Cut up the strawberries roughly. Place half of them in a blender or food processor and blitz for a few seconds to make a smooth purée. Sweeten with icing sugar and stir in the Cointreau.

2 Transfer the strawberry purée to a plastic container and cover with a lid or some clingfilm. Place in the freezer for about 2 hours until frozen and firm.

3 Briefly whizz the frozen strawberry mixture in a blender or processor and then fold into the fromage frais, swirling it attractively. Fold in the reserved chopped strawberries and crushed ratafias.

4 Line a 900 g/2 lb loaf tin with clingfilm, leaving plenty to overlap the edges of the tin. Pour the strawberry mixture into the lined tin and cover with clingfilm. Freeze for at least 3 hours until really firm.

5 When ready to serve, cut the frozen terrine into slices and decorate with whole strawberries.

SERVES four 170 7 2 banana yoghurt ice with exotic fruit coulis

Prep: **20** mins Freeze: **3+** hrs

3 ripe bananas
300 ml/½ pint low-fat natural yoghurt

Exotic fruit coulis:
1 ripe mango
2 ripe passion fruits
1 teaspoon icing sugar

1 Peel the bananas and cut them up roughly. Place the banana pieces in a blender with the yoghurt and blend to a smooth purée.

2 Pour the banana mixture into a plastic container and cover with a lid or clingfilm. Put in the freezer for 1 hour and then remove the container and beat the banana purée to break up the ice crystals and frozen edges. (Of course, if you have an ice-cream maker, follow the manufacturer's instructions and churn until frozen.)

3 Return to the freezer for another hour and then beat again, then freeze for at least 1 more hour until firm and frozen solid.

4 Meanwhile, make the coulis. Cut the mango in half and remove the outer peel. Cut away the ripe flesh from around the stone and place in a blender. Whizz to a purée.

5 Cut the passion fruits in half and scoop out the flesh and seeds. Mix with the mango purée and then push through a sieve to remove the seeds. Sweeten the coulis with icing sugar.

6 Remove the yoghurt ice from the freezer about 10 minutes before serving. Divide the scoops between 4 serving dishes or tall glasses and pour the exotic fruit coulis over the top.

vodka & lemon sorbet

serves six

Prep: **20** mins Cook: **14** mins Freeze: **3+** hrs

- **4 unwaxed lemons**
- **600 ml/1 pint water**
- **175 g/6 oz granulated sugar**
- **3 tablespoons vodka**

1 With a grater or lemon zester, finely grate the rind of 2 lemons into a bowl. Squeeze the juice of all the lemons and mix with the grated lemon zest.

2 Measure the water into a saucepan and add the sugar. Stir over a gentle heat until the sugar has completely dissolved.

3 Add the lemon zest and juice and bring to the boil. Boil for 1-2 minutes, then reduce the heat and cook for about 10 minutes. Set aside to cool.

4 When the syrup is totally cold, pour it into a plastic container and cover with a lid or some clingfilm. Freeze for about 2 hours, or until almost solid. If you have an ice cream maker, follow the manufacturer's instructions.

5 Remove from the freezer and beat well to break up the ice crystals. You can do this in a food processor if wished. Add the vodka and beat thoroughly.

6 Return to the freezer for at least 1 hour or until the sorbet is firm. You can make it a day or two in advance and leave it until required.

7 Remove from the freezer about 10 minutes before serving to allow the sorbet to soften a little. Scoop into balls and serve in pretty glasses - for a special occasion, you could even frost the edges.

SERVES
six **55** **2** **1**

blood orange
semi-freddo

Prep: **15** mins Freeze: **1** hr

2 medium to large blood oranges
150 ml/¼ pint low-fat natural yoghurt
1 tablespoon icing sugar
pinch of ground cinnamon
slivers of orange zest, to decorate
fresh summer fruits, e.g. strawberries, raspberries or
redcurrants, to serve

1 Carefully slice the top and bottom off each orange
and then remove the pith and peel from around the
sides.

2 With a small sharp knife, cut between the
membranes dividing the orange into segments and
remove the juicy segments.

3 Roughly chop the segments into small pieces and
spread them out on a freezer tray or plate.

4 Put the orange segments and the carton of yoghurt
in the freezer and freeze for at least 1 hour (overnight
if wished).

5 Put the frozen oranges, yoghurt, icing sugar and
cinnamon in a blender or food processor and blend
briefly, just for a few seconds. The mixture should stay
semi-frozen and retain some texture.

6 Spoon into bowls or glasses and decorate with
orange zest. Serve immediately with a selection of fresh
summer fruits.